MW00897256

I'm a Medicine Woman, Too!

Written and Illustrated by Jesse Wolf Hardin

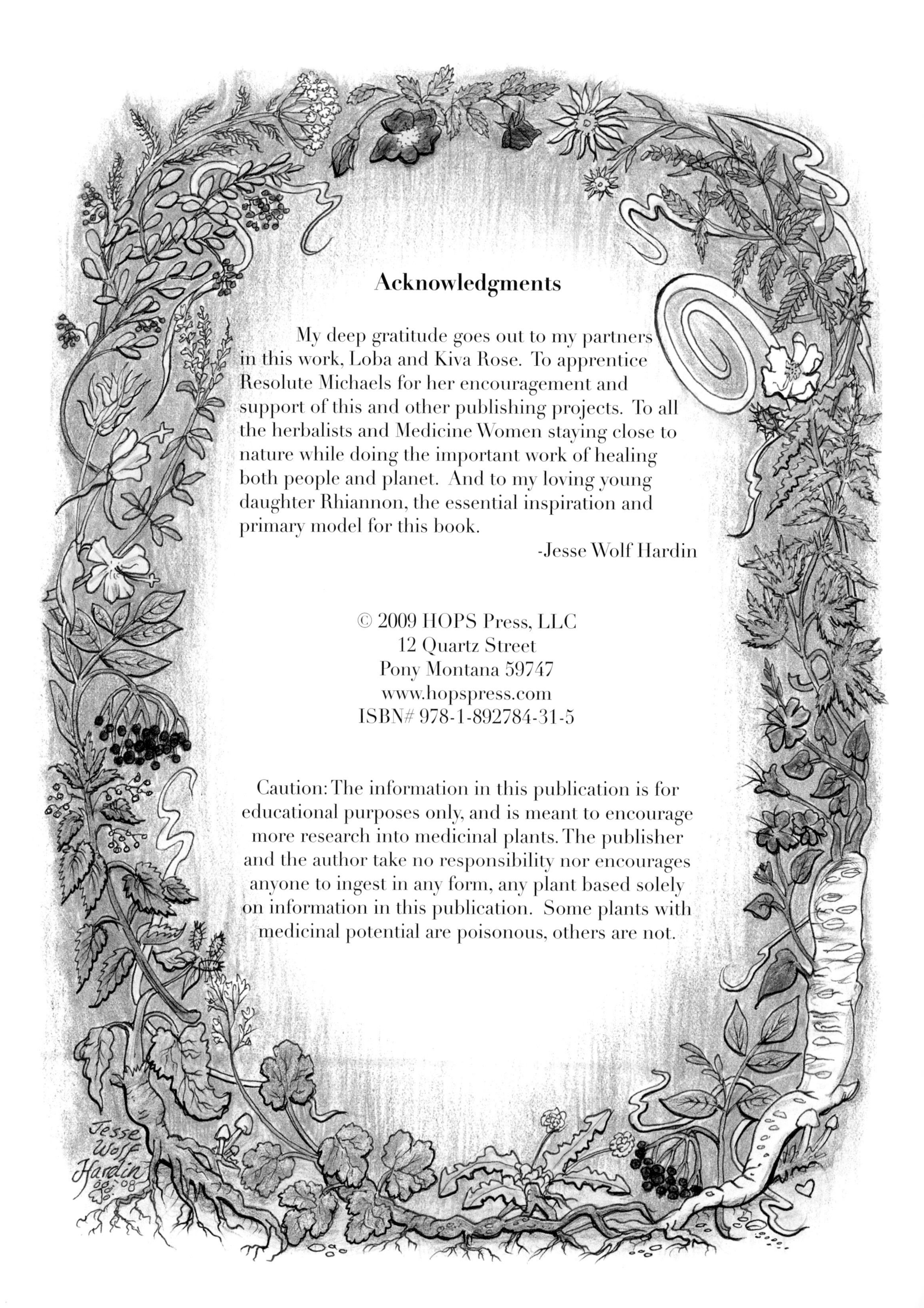

Acknowledgments

My deep gratitude goes out to my partners in this work, Loba and Kiva Rose. To apprentice Resolute Michaels for her encouragement and support of this and other publishing projects. To all the herbalists and Medicine Women staying close to nature while doing the important work of healing both people and planet. And to my loving young daughter Rhiannon, the essential inspiration and primary model for this book.

-Jesse Wolf Hardin

12 Quartz Street
Pony Montana 59747
www.hopspress.com
ISBN# 978-1-892784-31-5

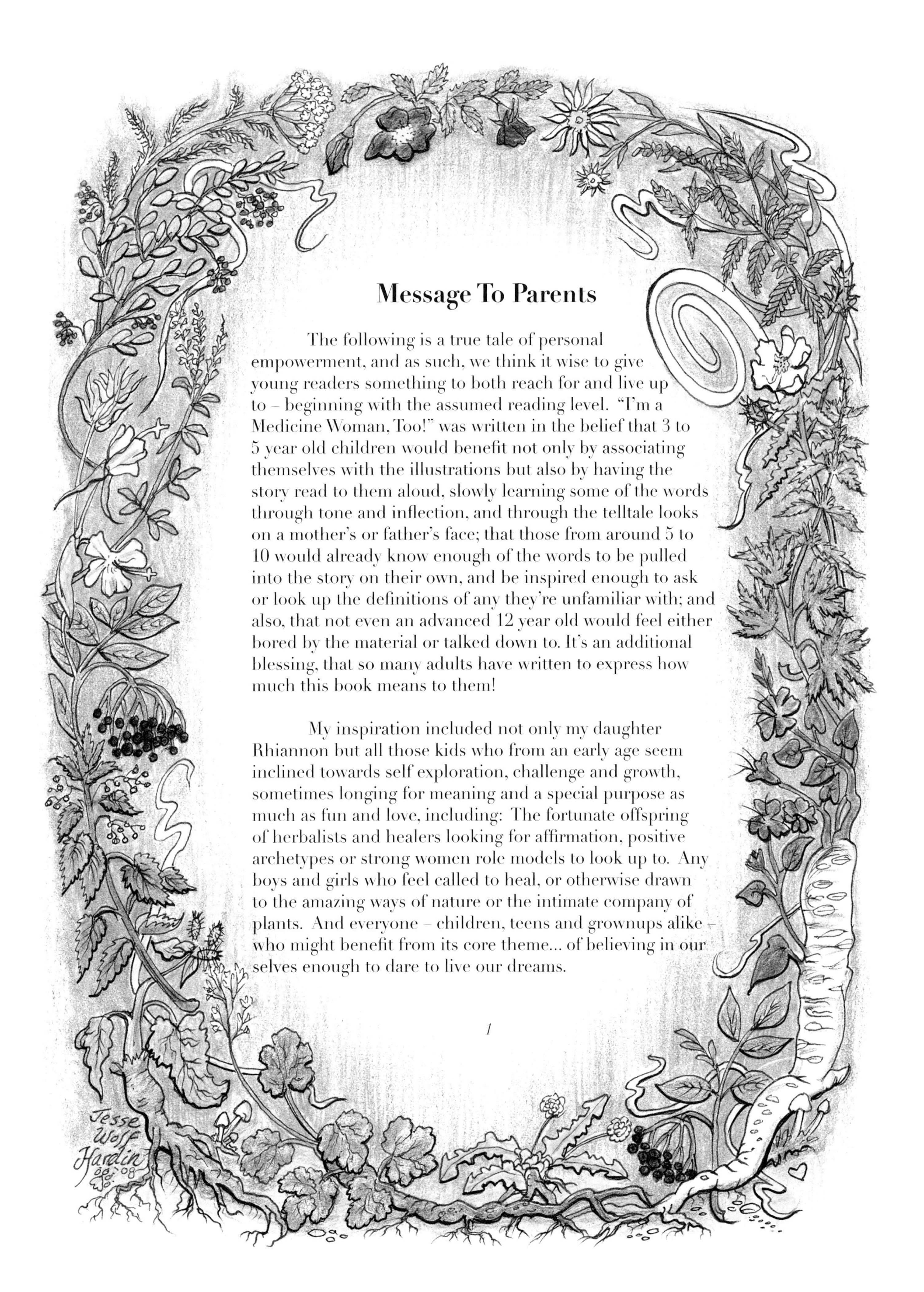

Message To Parents

The following is a true tale of personal empowerment, and as such, we think it wise to give young readers something to both reach for and live up to – beginning with the assumed reading level. "I'm a Medicine Woman, Too!" was written in the belief that 3 to 5 year old children would benefit not only by associating themselves with the illustrations but also by having the story read to them aloud, slowly learning some of the words through tone and inflection, and through the telltale looks on a mother's or father's face; that those from around 5 to 10 would already know enough of the words to be pulled into the story on their own, and be inspired enough to ask or look up the definitions of any they're unfamiliar with; and also, that not even an advanced 12 year old would feel either bored by the material or talked down to. It's an additional blessing, that so many adults have written to express how much this book means to them!

My inspiration included not only my daughter Rhiannon but all those kids who from an early age seem inclined towards self exploration, challenge and growth, sometimes longing for meaning and a special purpose as much as fun and love, including: The fortunate offspring of herbalists and healers looking for affirmation, positive archetypes or strong women role models to look up to. Any boys and girls who feel called to heal, or otherwise drawn to the amazing ways of nature or the intimate company of plants. And everyone – children, teens and grownups alike – who might benefit from its core theme... of believing in our selves enough to dare to live our dreams.

Anima
JESSE Wolf Hardin

At eight years of age, Rhiannon's life seemed to turn page by page like a fairy tale book, and not even she ever knew what was coming next.

Her home was a canyon with orange and purple cliffs studded with shiny bits of rock crystals. Coming there when she was four had truly been a dream come true! She loved sleeping in her special treehouse, imagining it even larger and more amazing than it was. It felt great waking up each morning to the sounds of elk singing and splashing in the river below. Living miles and miles from a town, she learned to follow the tracks of the deer and rabbits in her bare feet and talk to them all like friends. Her totem was the river otter, a very furry and playful animal, and just like the otter Rhiannon was always looking for a chance to play.

Then one day she came to me looking much more thoughtful than usual... and maybe just a little bit sad.

"What's the matter, my daughter?" I asked.

“I could never be a Medicine Woman like Mama Kiva or Mama Loba,” she answered with the cutest of pouts.

“No,” I told her, “but you could be a Medicine Woman that is the fulfillment of the real, whole you... like nobody else in the world can do.”

Anima
Medicine Woman Tradition
Wildcraft!
Jesse Wolf Hardin

"But Mama Loba somehow knows all the best herbs to add to the bestest meals," Rhiannon sighed. "And sometimes people come from far away just because of her and the special way that she makes them feel!"

"And Mama Kiva! She's always saying exactly what people need to hear, and knows what plants to suggest when they feel sick, or when they hurt themselves."

Seeing how upset she was, I got down on my knees to explain.

"Loba was born with a huge heart full of love," I said, "but she had to work for her other gifts. Kiva had to first learn from her mistakes, and then she had to choose to use her wisdom and skill for an important mission."

Rhiannon looked up with her shiny brown otter eyes.

"Besides," I said, "your gifts are already amazing! It's amazing how deeply you care and how hard you try. You often find the wild herbs we hunt for before anyone else does. You can sometimes tell if a person is unhappy, even if they try to hide it with a big smile on their face. You need to stop doubting your abilities, and fully believe in yourself."

“But I’m just a kid!”

"Little Sage is only five years old," I had to point out, "and already she bugs her mother to take her to the herb patch, learning about all kinds of plants like dandelion, goldenrod and milky oats."

“And give yourself some credit for what you have already learned and done!” I told her, as she followed me out onto the grass.

“You were born with only your animal instincts. You had to work hard to learn everything from how to talk to how to walk. You’ve already experienced people’s dishonesty, and that taught you the value and power of truth. You’ve done difficult things in order to get stronger, and taken risks in order to have adventure and fun. Just like a heroine on a legendary quest, you are always doing things that at first look impossible!”

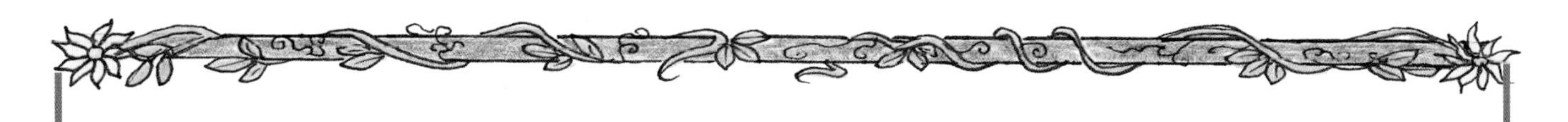

"Whether you know it or not," I continued, "you are part of a long chain of women and girls throughout history, reaching out hand to hand from mothers to daughters and teachers to students, from the most ancient human tribes right up until our modern day times.

"You can feel their hands in yours. They whisper sweet hints in the wind in the trees, in the yard or the shadowy far ends of a neighborhood park. They keep you company like faery friends helping you have wonderful dreams at night. These generations of Medicine Women want to teach you what you need. But even more importantly, they want to remind you of the strength and knowledge that you've already got."

"A Medicine Woman is not something you wait to become, it's what you do with your life, starting right now!"

"It wouldn't matter if your skin was brown or black, red or white. You've used the carved rock 'mano and metate' that we found, to grind seeds and herbs into powder just like the Medicine Women on the Apache reservation. And your little hands made the same motions over the stones as their great, great, great, great grandmothers once did."

JesseWolfHardin

"You've helped Mama Kiva dry and weigh chamomile and package bags of calendula for selling or trading, just as the Mexican curandera Doña Rosa does, selling herbs down a certain secret alleyway in her tiny Botanica shop. And when you dig up fresh dandelion roots for my liver decoction, remember that it's one of the fun tasks that the wrinkled old Doña was asked to do when she was still a little girl like you."

Yerba Buena
Jesse Wolf Hardin

"You tell people the things that they need to hear, just like our wise-woman friend Susun. And you grow catnip to help with belly aches, the same as Annie Mae at that Ozark Mountain herb farm that she runs."

Jesse Wolf-Hardin

Jesse
Wolf
Hardin

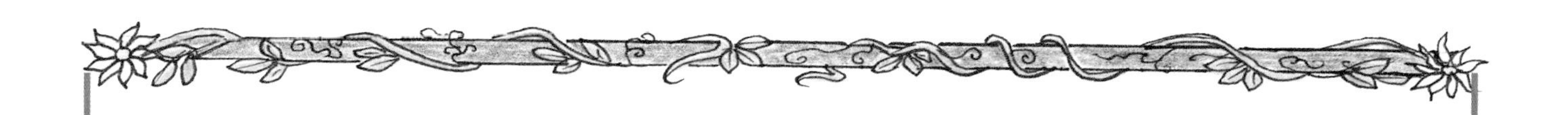

"It's the way of the Medicine Woman to love climbing into a mulberry tree high, gathering leaves for a lung tonic and berries for a pie. To work hard and be proud of what you do, while playing until you're silly, too! Doing what you can to offer people help, but also remembering to take special care of yourself. Collecting lots of grapes to preserve for the Winter, before the songbirds fly south... but also taking time to pop a few into your mouth."

"Remember: A Medicine Woman is anyone who is dedicated to healing her self, other people and the planet that we are a part of. She uses more than just a press for making tinctures and the mortar and pestle that she grinds her herbs in. Her tools include empathy, which means her ability to feel what others feel. And her deep compassion, which is how very much she cares about people and the land, and how concerned she is when they hurt. She brings the blessings of nature to the hearts of people in their cities, and brings the healing ways of thousands of years ago into the light of today."

Jesse
Wolf
Hardin

"But," Rhiannon replied, "medicine women sound so very special and magical."

Anima
Jesse Wolf Hardin

"And so are you," I insisted. "You are the first to notice the shapes of animals in the clouds above. The butterflies fly right up to you, and not a single creature or even a shift in the wind goes by unnoticed. When I'm upset about something, it only takes one of your very magical hugs to make everything feel alright again."

Anima
Jesse Wolf Hardin

“You need to see yourself for who you really are inside,” I said a little while later, handing Rhiannon a box of colored pencils and a clean sheet of paper.

“Try drawing a picture of yourself in all your strength and wonder, dressed up as the Medicine Woman – or any other woman of power – that you are meant to be. Then, do things in life the way the girl you drew would do.”

"In this way, you create your own place within the honorable Medicine Woman Tradition."

Anima
Jesse Wolf
Hardin

"But what if I decide I don't want to be a healer?" she asked me with a look. "What if I want to be something else, like a warrior defending the helpless, a great singer or cook?"

"You can be all that and more," I answered. "You have a choice in everything you do, and it is your responsibility what you yourself choose. You might decide to plant trees and restore wild places, change the world with the power of your artwork, grow organic food, or teach eager students at a school like Animá Center."

"Dancing is a way to open hearts and mend spirits, and Ananda takes time away from her herbal practice to still do it some. Sister Osha helps people on journeys of healing by leading vision quests, playing powerful rhythms on her medicine drum."

Jesse
Wolf Hardin

"You'll find your own way and develop new abilities and skills as you go along. But the first step is for you to honor and make good use of the many blessings you already have."

"The job of the Medicine Woman isn't just to heal sickness," I added, "but to help make everything healthier and more beautiful. Each woman works in her own personal ways to both create and improve the world. Each follows her heart, knows her purpose, and answers her special calling. And each must be brave enough to live her wildest dreams, no matter how hard that ever seems."

"In that case, it must be true..."
my little girl said.

"I'm a Medicine Woman, too!"

Name The Herb Game

Here's a fun game to try, after you've read the story. All of the plants shown here are well known for their medicinal uses, most (though not all) are found wild in the mountain and desert West, and you can read about them in popular herb books. Write your answers down on a separate piece of paper, along with any medicinal uses for the plants that you might remember. Then turn to the Game Answer chart on page 43 for the correct answers.

Page 6:

What is the name of the tasty, wonderful smelling purple flowers that Loba is cooking with?

Page 7:

A) What are the large purple flowers called, above Kiva's right hand? Hint: it's in the mint family, and bees really love it!

B) Right beneath those big purple flowers, are some tiny blue flowers that some herbalists use to help people sleep. What's their name?

C) The lovely looking yellow flower in the bowl opens in the evenings and turns pinkish or orange as it wilts. Guess what its name is.

D) The plant with blue berries, in the bowl below Kiva's bear claw necklace, is good for the liver. It has bright yellow flowers, the same color as their roots. What's its name?

E) What is the name of the tall, cream colored flowers above Kiva's left hand? They are great for treating cuts and wounds, and are some of the earliest known plant medicines ever used by people.

Page 10:

A) Name the grassy plants that Rhiannon's young friend has in her arms. It's a popular nerve tonic.

B) Name the tall plant with big leaves and stickery seed pods with dark purple hairs. It has an edible sweet root and is a common liver herb.

C) The dark red flowers below Sage's arm help with pain as well as help you sleep. What are they?

D) Below the log on the right is one of the most popular adaptogens and a common wild food with many of the nutrients we need to survive and be healthy. Warning: There's a reason that it is usually harvested with gloves on!

Page 15:

Name this Southwestern herb, a relative of the common mallow often used as a sticky poultice or tea by the Indians and Hispanics of this region.

Page 16:

Name the plant Rhiannon is picking. Its leaves are a great bitter salad green and its roots make a popular liver relaxant. Hint: Every kid loves to blow on the fuzzy round seed clusters, then watch them fly away on the wind.

Page 17:

A) On the ceiling above this New Mexican herbalist are some yellow and white flowers used to make tea to settle children's upset bellies. Do you know what it is called?

B) Below her arm on the table are orange flowers used to treat wounds and assist the immune system. What are they called?

Page 18:

This smelly plant is good for stomach aches and fevers, and certain kinds of household pets are just crazy about it! Meow!

Page 19:

The plants in the peat pots are sage babies. What are the little bluish-purple flowered plants below this gardener's feet? The flowers make a sweet syrup as well as famous perfume, and the leaves are moistening and often used to add yummy flavor to salads. Some people call them "shy"...

Page 20:

Rhiannon is holding a potted plant that smells like a favorite kind of citrus fruit. It makes a yummy tea as well as an effective tincture for the nerves. What is it?

Page 21:

What are these delicious wild fruits Rhiannon is gathering? Everyone knows they make great desserts and jams, but they are also effective as a blood tonic. The leaves are used in a poultice for swelling as well as made into a paste for bug bites.

Page 22:

In the bear paw print bowl is a plant smoked by Native Americans, with edible red berries and leaves that are used to ease bladder infections. Can you figure out its name?

Page 23:

The plant in Kiva's hand makes an unequaled immune tonic to help us keep colds away. The berries make wonderful wine and jam, and are found on bushes that can grow up to twenty feet tall. Can you name it?

Page 24:

The clear gel inside this succulent is often used to treat burns and wounds. It's not native to America, but is popular as a potted plant. What is its name?

Page 25:

Can you tell what the plant is with the pinkish-purple flowers in Kiva's hand? This aromatic cooking herb is often used to reduce fever and ease stomach aches, as well as to treat wounds and steady nerves.

Page 29:

Do you know what the pink flowers are, with five petals and yellow centers? Hint: Rhiannon always wears gloves when she picks them so that she doesn't get poked by all the thorns!

Page 32:

The plant and root below this Medicine Woman is a kind of wild licorice, used for the lungs by herbalists in China and elsewhere. Another classic lung herb is the tall plant growing next to her, with soft fuzzy leaves and a tall seed stalk. What's its name?

Page 35:

Rhiannon is holding a plant which has yellow flowers. What is the name of the other plant she is holding, the one with the feathery purple flowers? Hint: It is used to treat coughs and congestion as well as common allergies.

Jesse
Wolf Hardin

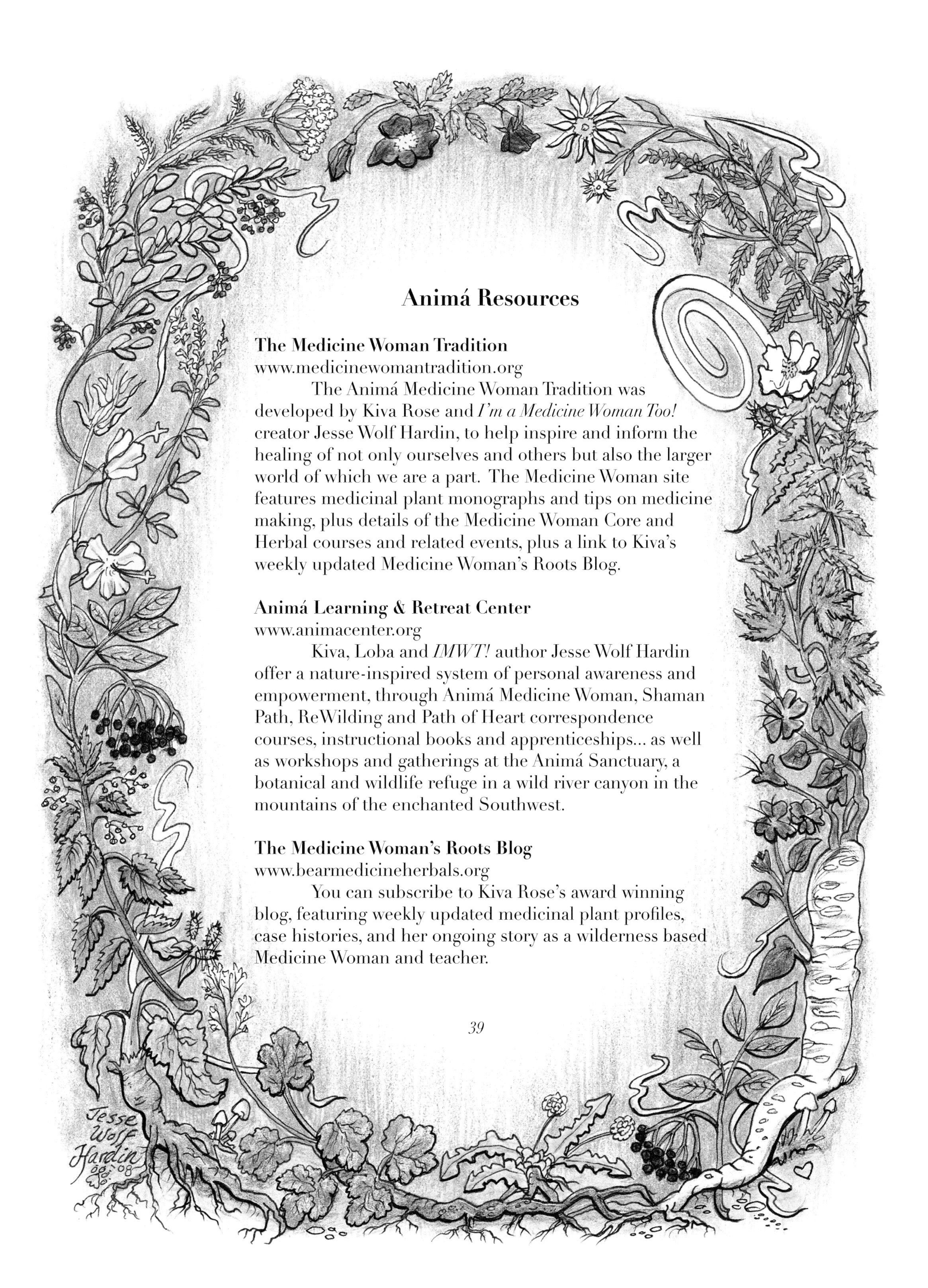

Animá Resources

The Medicine Woman Tradition
www.medicinewomantradition.org

The Animá Medicine Woman Tradition was developed by Kiva Rose and *I'm a Medicine Woman Too!* creator Jesse Wolf Hardin, to help inspire and inform the healing of not only ourselves and others but also the larger world of which we are a part. The Medicine Woman site features medicinal plant monographs and tips on medicine making, plus details of the Medicine Woman Core and Herbal courses and related events, plus a link to Kiva's weekly updated Medicine Woman's Roots Blog.

Animá Learning & Retreat Center
www.animacenter.org

Kiva, Loba and *IMWT!* author Jesse Wolf Hardin offer a nature-inspired system of personal awareness and empowerment, through Animá Medicine Woman, Shaman Path, ReWilding and Path of Heart correspondence courses, instructional books and apprenticeships... as well as workshops and gatherings at the Animá Sanctuary, a botanical and wildlife refuge in a wild river canyon in the mountains of the enchanted Southwest.

The Medicine Woman's Roots Blog
www.bearmedicineherbals.org

You can subscribe to Kiva Rose's award winning blog, featuring weekly updated medicinal plant profiles, case histories, and her ongoing story as a wilderness based Medicine Woman and teacher.

Sweet Medicine Books

All books and available from: Kiva Rose, PO Box 688, Reserve, NM 87830, or to contribute through PayPal go to www.animacenter.org/donate.html and note which title or item you are ordering.

The Way Of Animá: Nature-Informed Insights & Forgotten Wisdom
by Jesse Wolf Hardin

Concise aphorisms, redefinitions and clarifications serving as inspiring reminders or daily meditations. This unique collection is made up of concise 2 to 8 line sections, arranged according to themes. Each short passage is meant to be able to stand alone, so that it's possible to turn to any page seemingly at random and put your finger on an inspiring – and sometimes surprisingly timely or relevant – "daily thought" for your consideration and application. $25.00 suggested donation

The Medicine Bear (Novel) by Jesse Wolf Hardin

An adult historical romance, set in the American West in 1916, at a time when the both the natural world and Old West ways were undergoing a radical change. Characters include a strong willed herbalist both as a child and adult, her flamboyant nature writer husband, the influential ecologist Aldo Leopold and a wonderful traditional Medicine Woman by the name of Doña Rosa. This sweeping epic is filled with plant and nature lore, setting the context for the lead couple's uncompromised vision and unconquerable love. $25.00 suggested donation.

Home: Reinhabating Self, Place & Purpose
by Jesse Wolf Hardin

An inspiring book providing the perceptual and practical tools needed for becoming more at home in our deeply feeling bodies, our communities and cultures, the specific bioregions where we live and in the larger natural world in general. In the process, Hardin describes his own journey from youthful gypsy to lifelong caretaker of a magical river canyon and botanical sanctuary, covering topics like restoring wildlands and planting our yards with native species, eating wild, awakening our senses. “We are not rootless, but uprooted,” the author explains. To help us heal the wounds of our distancing, Hardin offers detailed suggestions for reconnecting with both our natural selves and the natural world of which we are a part, describing how to find that specific place that will best serve our spirits and growth, as well as how to be consciously and actively “at home” wherever we might find ourselves. $25.00 suggested donation.

The Gifting Bones: A Nature-Informed Runic System

Jesse Wolf Hardin’s original Animá inspired Runes, inspired and informed by the principles and lessons of the real, natural world.

The 18 two-sided, handmade porcelain “bones” come in a lovely cloth bag with a detailed user’s manual. 4 Bones are drawn from the bag for each reading and laid out from left to right, representing our in-the-moment relationship with Self, Others, Nature and Spirit (or the Anima), speaking not of the future but the always momentous present. The Bones are amazingly powerful and telling tools with which can help you clarify the criteria and circumstances relevant to every conscious choice you will ever face. $38.00 suggested donation

Other Resources

Herbmentor – http://herbmentor.com

John and Kimberly Gallagher's phenomenal site for herbalists of all ages and abilities. Accessible, down to earth and straightforward, this interactive site includes forums, audio & video lessons, interviews with well known herbalists and many other amazing opportunities.

Earth School http://www.lovetheearth.com

The Earth School teaches an array of outdoor awareness classes, including workshops on edible and medicinal plants, fire making, tracking, nature crafts and much more.

Susun Weed – http://susunweed.com

A powerful learning experience for adults, Susun Weed encourages self nourishment, wholeness and independent exploration.

Rosemary Gladstar/Sage Mountain – http://sagemountain.com

Rosemary's wisdom and teachings continue to inspire new generations of herbalists. Her classes, correspondence course and sanctuary are highly recommended.

A Kid's Herb Book by Lesley Tierra

A well thought out guide to herbalism for children, including songs, plant profiles and lots of fun activities.

Coyote's Guide to Connecting with Nature by Young, Haas & McGown

A provocative guide to awareness, belonging and connection with nature for children and their mentors.

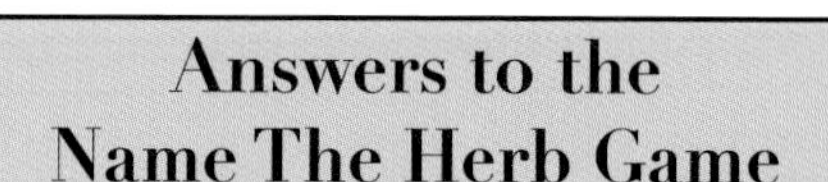

Answers to the Name The Herb Game

Page 6: Lavender
Page 7:
- A: Monarda (Bee Balm)
- B: Skullcap
- C: Evening Primrose
- D: Oregon Grape
- E: Yarrow

Page 10:
- A: Milky Oats
- B: Burdock
- C: Corn Poppy
- D: Nettles

Page 15: Globe Mallow
Page 16: Dandelion
Page 17:
- A: Chamomile
- B. Calendula (Marigold)

Page 18: Catnip
Page 19: Violets
Page 20: Lemon Balm
Page 21: Wild Grapes
Page 22: K'nick-K'nick (Uva Ursi, or Bear Berry)
Page 23: Elderberry
Page 24: Aloe Vera
Page 25: Garden Sage
Page 29: Wild Rose
Page 32: Mullein
Page 35: Yerba Santa

Looking for an easier way to learn to identify plants?

Shanleya's Quest
A Botany Adventure for Kids Ages 9 to 99

By Thomas J. Elpel Illustrated by Gloria Brown

In a world where time is a liquid that falls as rain upon the land, young Shanleya paddles her canoe out to the Tree Islands to learn the plant traditions of her people. Each island is home to a separate family of plants and an unforgettable Guardian with lessons to teach about the identification and uses of those plants. Shanleya's Quest is a truly unique educational book that presents botanical concepts and plant identification skills in an easy and fun metaphorical format for children, as well as for adults who are young at heart.

Read the book. Play the game!
Book: 2005. ISBN: 1-892784-16-5. 32 pages. $12.50
Game: 2006. ISBN: 1-892784-23-8. 52 cards. $12.50

Botany in a Day
The Patterns Method of Plant Identification

Thomas J. Elpel's Herbal Field Guide to Plant Families of North America

Botany in a Day is changed the way people learn about plants! Elpel's book has gained a nationwide audience almost exclusively by word-of-mouth. It is now used as a text and recommended by herbal schools and universities across North America. Instead of presenting individual plants, Botany in a Day unveils the patterns of identification and uses among related plants, giving readers simple tools to rapidly unlock the mysteries of new species they encounter throughout North America. Too often people try to learn plants one-at-a-time without rhyme or reason, but now you can cut years off the process of learning about plants and their uses. Botany in a Day takes you beyond the piecemeal approach to botany and herbalism towards a "whole" approach. Within 1 1/2 hours you can understand the big picture of botany and herbalism. Learn how relatedplants have similar features for identification. Discover how they often have similar properties and similar uses.

Tom's book takes you beyond the details towards a greater understanding of the patterns among plants. By mid-morning you can be in the field, matching flowers to the patterns in the book. Instead of learning plants one-at-a-time, you will discover that you can learn them by the dozens—just by looking for patterns. Most plant books cover only one or two hundred species. Botany in a Day includes more than 100 plant families and over 700 genera—applicable to many thousands of species. Four indexes. 5th Edition. 2004. ISBN: 1-892784-15-7. 221 pages. 100% recycled paper. $30.

Go to **www.hopspress.com** to order and to browse all our titles!

Praise For This Book

"I believe I'm holding a new children's classic, a book that will be treasured by children – and their parents -- for years to come. This is a beautifully written story of a child's quest for her own magical gifts and her place in the circle of 'medicine women'. The story unfolds by Rhiannon, the little girl of the tale, asking the questions of how one becomes a 'medicine woman' and her search for what her special purpose in the world is. There is simple earth wisdom in the answers that are offered, and teachings about the plants and healing scattered throughout that are sure to enchant any young nature lover. But what makes this book really stand out are the lush illustrations of plants, nature, goddesses, our little seeker Rhiannon, and the special 'medicine women' in her life. While the story is lovely and inspiring in itself, the colorful drawings add a special touch that is sure to appeal to every child who has ever lingered in a field of wildflowers or asked the questions, either aloud or quietly, 'where is my place in the circle of life?' 'What are my special gifts?' Jesse Wolf Hardin has written a book that will inspire children to fully believe in themselves and to reach for their own unique dreams"

- **Rosemary Gladstar,** Herbalist and author of *The Family Herbal*

"*I'm a Medicine Woman, Too!* is a wonderful book to connect children with herbal traditions. The story role-models an ethic of healing and caring for other people and honoring our elders. The delightful illustrations touch the reader at an emotional level, compelling us to become healers too."

-**Thomas J. Elpel**, author of *Botany in a Day* and *Shanleya's Quest: A Botany Adventure for Kids Ages 9 to 99.*

"*I'm a Medicine Woman, Too!* is full of wisdom, beauty and encouragement not only for young girls, but for women of all ages. The author's exquisite illustrations quickly draw the reader in and cleverly teach about healing plants. A high recommendation for empowering all medicine women!"

-**Lesley Tierra,** L. Ac., author of *Healing with the Herbs of Life* and *A Kid's Herb Book.*

"I felt the voice of the Earth Mother Herself speak from the pages of *I'm A Medicine Woman, Too!* The sense of presence and higher awareness will benefit younger audiences and those with accumulated years as well. A fine offering to raise consciousness!"

-**Margi Flint** AHG HM, Author of *The Practicing Herbalist*

"Today, my daughter Hailey and I read *I'm a Medicine Woman, Too!* by Jesse Wolf Hardin. What a wonderful, sweet story! As I was reading I kept thinking, this is a story Hailey and I will read together again and again. Hailey is only four right now. At this age she loved the beautiful illustrations, and wanted to know the names of each of the women in the pictures. When we finished reading she brought out two of her dolls so we could play medicine woman. We spent time together pretending to mix medicines for different ailments. It was so fun to see how the story spurred her imagination. With two parents who are herbalists, this was an easy story for Hailey to identify with. I know as she grows older the themes about believing in herself and finding and trusting her gifts will resonate more deeply, and I look forward to reading the story again and again. This is just the kind of story I want my children hearing over and over – the kind of story that will help them grow into themselves with grace and beauty."

-**Kimberly Gallagher**, M.Ed., CCH, LearningHerbs.com & HerbMentor.com

"A book thoroughly enjoyed by both myself and my little boys, "*I'm a Medicine Woman, Too*" entices us not to look to others for ourselves, but rather to go within and bring out what we are, and know in doing so that we give the world around us what it needs. That such an important insight is accompanied by such beautiful images makes this book even more of a treasure."

-**Jim McDonald,** Herbalist and teacher